WELCO

to YOUR **TEACHING** doodle book!

Board Pen.

Gue Stick

This book is designed to be a diary for your thoughts and a scrapbook for your memories - the book you'll keep in your bag all year.
It's full of ideas, activities and survival tips for you to absorb, add to and **share!**

A quick note about me & the author

Paul Wright (@Pw2tweets)

Job: I'm Head of IT at a large secondary school so I understand the pressures of the classroom and those that come with leadership.
I'm a teacher because I love helping learners to learn and teachers to teach!

Grab a pen, turn the page and let's start the year together!

The CONTENTS

of your doodle book...

TAKE A SELFIE

TERM:

5

1st day Nerves
I don't want to go to School tomorrow!
You have to. You're the teacher now!
Everyone is nervous about their first day!
Try and remember this.
make your 1st day list here

PACK YOUR BAG

Make sure you have more than one white board pen in your bag.

Board Pen
Board Pen
Board Pen

Possibly one of the most versitle resources you can have!!

Sticky notes

Have plenty of pencils in your bag, for students who will forget.

Tip: Check out the sticky note ideas pages in this book

Highlighters
- Always have these. Great tools!

Tip → Simplify marking by using green to highlight good things you read in a student's work. Red/amber to highlight areas to review/improve.

Pack for Well being

Buy a new bottle of water to keep with you each week.

Keep some throat sweets in your bag at all times

COUGH, COUGH

You'll need them i...

trendy teachers.

and what not to wear for work!

TRENDY

Don't wear clothes with swear words or offensive slogans!

This is never appropriate for a school!

*!#? MY WEEK!!

Doodle your own subject t-shirt design!

This type of fun t-shirt is exactly what to wear on a non-uniform day!

Science Rocks!

IF YOU'RE GOING TO WEAR A SLOGAN SHIRT TO WORK MAKE SURE IT'S CLEAN + FUN!!

FOR NON-UNIFORM DAYS THINK:

☐ Practical
☐ Fun
☐ Appropriate

MASTER COPY

THINGS TO LEARN

- COPIER CAPABILITIES:
  - → BOOKLETS
  - → BACK-TO-BACK
- KEEP AN EYE ON HOW MUCH YOU SPEND!
- PLAN YOUR BULK COPYING IN ADVANCE!

GOLDEN RULES

- IF YOU'VE LOTS TO COPY TRY TO DO IT AT A QUIET TIME – NOT DURING THE MORNING RUSH!
- IF THE COPIER JAMS OR BREAKS DOWN → REPORT IT!

Learn to LOVE the Photocopier

ORGANISING YOUR MEMORY STICK

tips for keeping organised...

Organise by term or ½ term

Organise by subject area.

Organise by responsibility area.

Organise by teaching group

keep it secret, keep it safe!

DON'T save your personal files & photos onto the same USB stick you take to work!

NQTs

THINGS
You NEED
TO KNOW...

There's lots to know about the NQT year. Here are 3 key facts to start with...

Now you have QTS you must complete the 12 month Induction NQT year in order to teach as a qualified teacher in the UK.

At the end of the NQT year your head teacher will sign you off having met the teaching standards if you are successful.

You cannot serve your NQT induction year in a school on Special Measures!

Ways to organise NQT evidence...

TEACHING STANDARDS...

Tips...

Ⓛ Make time to update your evidence every 2 weeks!

📅12 Use a friday afternoon to update your evidence.

💬 Talk to other NQTs about their approach.

☑ Use the Standards to structure your folder.

GOOD EVIDENCE...

👓 lesson observation records - Highlight key feedback comments which link to areas you developed.

📄 Annotated resources you have used/created.

▦ Data analysed to track/inform pupil progress.

What does next week hold?

★ Highlight of the week?

Administration

Extra Curricular?

Work life balance

other notes

YOUR DAY AS A PIZZA...

HOW MUCH IS ON YOUR PLATE?

Carve the pizza up with your average day...

SUBJECT KNOWLEDGE

HOW TO KEEP UP TO DATE...

 TEACH NOW

magazines and trade press.

 WEBSITES BLOGS

 SOCIAL MEDIA

 SUBJECT AND STAGE SPECIFIC SOCIAL GATHERINGS.

make a note of your sources of subject knowledge. →

ROUTINES SAVE YOU FROM STRESS!
"Coats off as you come into the room!"
"Always have a pen ready!"
"Hands up to ask questions!"
"Equipment monitor names are on the display board for this week!"
Tip
Number spare pens using sticky tape and paper!
1
"Pens are in the usual pen pot!"

Good **Starters**

GRAB attention!

ENGAGE Minds

INSPIRE learners

Kick start your lessons with good Starters!

Starter activities are VITAL components of every Lesson!

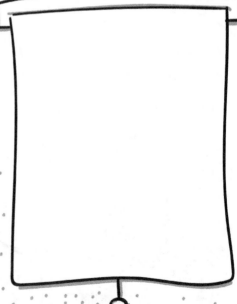

Write down your best Starter ideas here

Good starter activities should...

INSPIRE

GRAB

INTRODUCE

ENGAGE

Best starter activity I've seen this ½ term.

WHAT I SAW 👁 👁 ...

ME

WHEN I SAW THIS Ⓛ ...

IMPACT ON MY TEACHING...

Wow factors

What do you do to grab students' attention?

Start a lesson with a slide show related to the topic

Collect your own *wow* factor ideas here

Start a Science lesson with a *wow*!

Questioning ? tips

Using an ordinary box as your 'hook' Plan an activity using Blooms questioning to engage learners in a questioning activity.

Challenge learners to answer the question "what's in the box?" using Vocabulary from every level of BLOOM'S taxonomy for questioning.

BLOOM'S TAXONOMY A hierachy of thinking skills!

Starting with KNOWLEDGE and Moving to

COMPREHENSION SYNTHESIS and EVALUATION!

Ideas

Spotlight...

Create moments that
hook learners!

- Using a hit song
  to link to a topic.
- Showing a TV show
  clip.

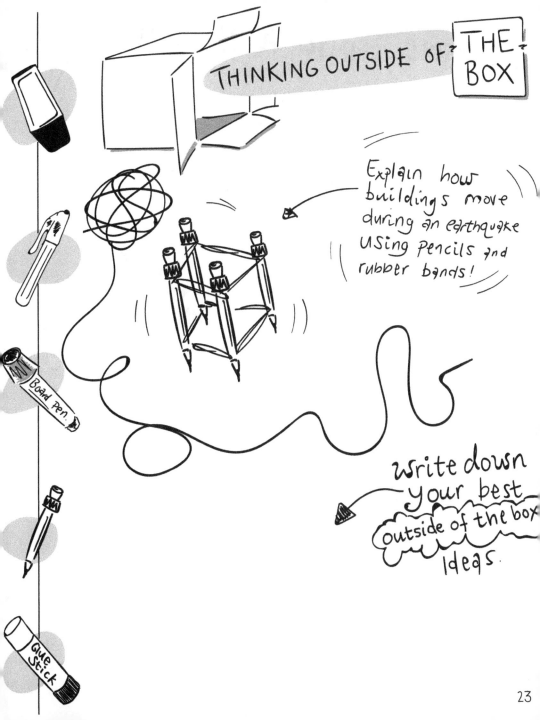

GETTING INTO A ROLE TO ENGAGE

I've seen some skilled and brave teachers use role play to engage both top and bottom set students. Primary teachers use this a lot, but you can use role play to effectively engage Secondary School students.

Pick a class, be brave, and get into a role to engage your learners!!

Then use this space to record your achievements!

Teach history as a WW2 Pilot!!

It's 1066 and I'm having a very bad day!!

Teach Science as a MAD Scientist!!

Give me an **A**!

A make up your own acronyms.

CLASSROOM DISPLAYS...

Use **BRIGHT** colours which stand out!

Use clear and **BOLD** fonts which are easy to read!

Use strong images which learners will easily relate to!

Get learners involved in creating the display!

Use this space to design a display in your class.

USING ICT IN YOUR CLASS...

Make full use of technology you're used to.

Even little things like learning to ⏸ Pause/freeze the projector image can be super useful!

Use online tutorials to help you keep your own skills up-to-date!

This will help your confidence when using tech with learners

Fully research and test out new tech before using it in class!

Start with tech you know, like cameras. Use these to ennance learning!

27

The Holiday Season

No matter which holiday, if you can celebrate it then do!

Learning is as much about emotional response to stimulation as it is about knowing facts and figures.

what does the holiday mean to them?

what can learners share about the holiday?

what can they learn about the holiday?

what can learners create relating to this holiday?

DESIGN YOUR IDEAL CLASSROOM

if finance was not a problem,
what would your ideal classroom contain?

31

find ideas in unusual places and Stick them here...

fill the Page!

Use coloured sticky notes like traffic lights on desks or PCs.

Use sticky notes as easy exit tickets in lessons.

Use sticky notes as spelling practice slips at the start of a lesson.

Reveal answers on a board or worksheet by covering them with sticky notes.

Can you add your own ideas..?

Continue to add your sticky note ideas on this page.

35

"cheap"
easy
effective!

36

GET OUTSIDE YOUR ROOM...

When the bell rings!

Be seen as part of the school teaching team

Meet and talk to the students not in your classes.

Help to manage student behaviour

Reasons to be outside your classroom as often as possible.

Meet with colleagues who you don't regularly work with.

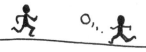

Breaktime duty

TOP TIPS FOR A SUCCESSFUL BREAK DUTY EXPERIENCE...

 HAVE A MUG WITH A LID!

 KEEP A SCARF IN YOUR OFFICE READY FOR COLD DAYS!

CONSIDER A HAT TOO!

KNOW THE DAYS AND TIMES OF YOUR DUTIES.

PUT A REMINDER IN YOUR PHONE OR POCKET DIARY!

 KNOW THE LOCATION OF YOUR DUTIES AND A ROUTE IF YOU'VE SPACE TO COVER.

 ALWAYS BE SMILING!

39

At break times and in lessons be vigilant, accidents do happen. Keep in mind...

Follow procedure. **Hand book**

If unsure, always speak to someone!

Report any incidents

...and... document them.

Communicate with parents.

injury at School (don't panic!)

make a note of who to go to...

Educational Visits

Educational visits can bring subjects to life, engage learners and can help staff and students to form bonds.

EXTRA CURRICULAR

Comic books

Comic Adventures

THEN 34

Music

Art

rom Sharing
a personal Passion
ike film, books or art, to teaching a skill outside the curriculum
getting Involved in extra curricular activities is encouraged!

I ran a film-making club after School. kids from Y.9 - 13 got to make movies. It was awesome.

Action

Write ideas down

Preparing for an OBSERVATION

Don't Panic!!

No stunts!!

It's tempting to 'perform' in an observation. We see observations as being about ourselves, but the true focus is always on the learner!

1. Progress
2. Engagement
3. Differentiation

3 words KEY to Success!!

Focus on these when you plan!

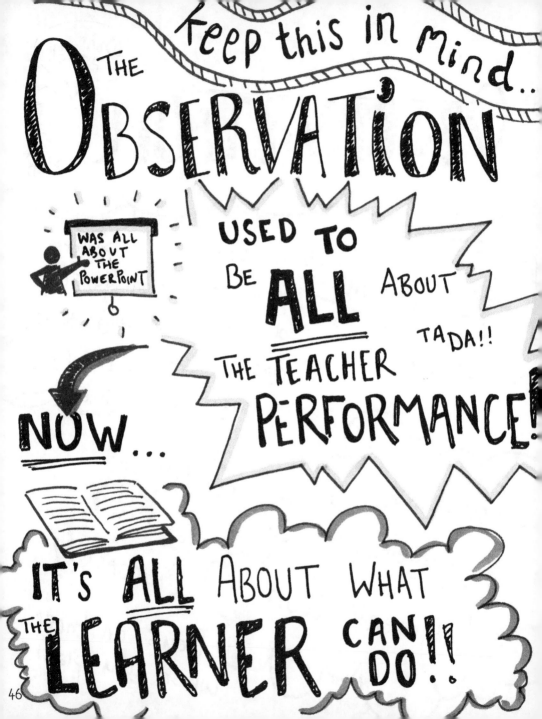

CREATE YOUR OWN 'USEFUL BOX'!

Praise Reward

Stamps

Sticky-notes

Stickers!

Box of Tricks

LOTS of Pens!

what would you put in?

Making an OBSERVATION easier!

by ensuring that everyone moves forward.

Sign Post

the progress being made

Progress

The biggest Buzz word in teaching!

But an important one!!

For me, securing good progress means using SMART differentiation activities so that every learner is stretched and challenged.

Check out these options

Option 1

Explain...

Take today's topic and explain it using key vocabulary.

Option 2

Explain + Examples

Using key vocabulary explain today's topic and support your explanation with examples.

Option 3

Explain + Examples + Evaluate

Explain todays topic using key vocabulary and example. Then evaluate today's work using given criteria

Making an OBSERVATION easier.

No one is an island.

Engagement

To engage learners- don't assume that you have to know it all alone. Seek ideas and inspiration from others. Write down ideas here.

making an Observation easier.

Differentiation

Helping everyone to achieve their potential isn't easy, seek ideas from others...

write down any tips you are given.

YOUR BEST
OBSERVATION...

WHY...

ACTIONS TO TAKE...

YOUR WORST
OBSERVATION...

WHY...

ACTIONS TO TAKE...

Remember, good and bad observations
are about making progress.

Dealing with **TOUGH** Feedback

Sometimes lessons don't go to plan. We've all had these lessons, what's most important is that you learn from them!

WWW EB/

LEARN from the conversations you have. Just as you ask learners to reflect, you should too. Ask yourself 'what went well?' AND would it be 'even better if?'

Take any constructive criticism as an opportunity to REFLECT and improve

Be open to revisiting your plans with a critical eye

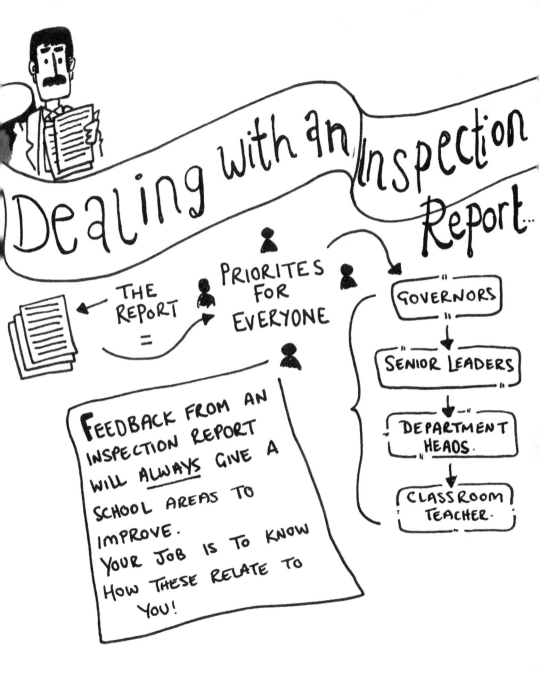

Dealing with an Inspection Report...

THE REPORT =

PRIORITES FOR EVERYONE

GOVERNORS

↓

SENIOR LEADERS

↓

DEPARTMENT HEADS.

↓

CLASSROOM TEACHER.

FEEDBACK FROM AN INSPECTION REPORT WILL <u>ALWAYS</u> GIVE A SCHOOL AREAS TO IMPROVE.
YOUR JOB IS TO KNOW HOW THESE RELATE TO YOU!

I AM NOT A NUMBER!

DATA can be a real headache!

It is important to know how to use data properly.

In this section we're looking at the person behind the data.

NAME THESE LEARNERS

✳ COLOUR IN THEIR SHIRTS!

HOW DO YOU SUPPORT THESE LEARNERS IN YOUR CLASSES?

Days are long and busy but try and learn about your students. Knowing them will help you to support, inspire and engage them.

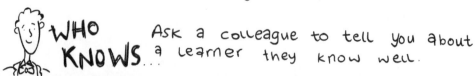

WHO KNOWS... Ask a colleague to tell you about a learner they know well.

Getting to know you...

Your LIKES

Draw yourself

DISLIKES

FUN FACTS...

Favourite Colour.

FAVOURITE FILM...

A BOOK ENJOYED...

Photocopy this sheet for students

Seating Plans

FACE PARTNER

SHOULDER PARTNER

OR

SEAT BY DATA eg...

WHICH CLASSES CAN YOU TRY THESE WITH...

"PUPIL PREMIUM"

"HATT"

Why is this student **ANGRY**?

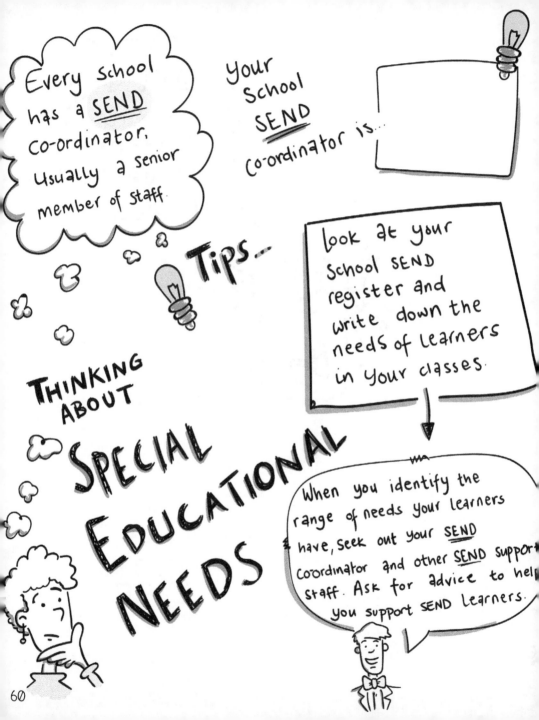

Every school has a **SEND** Co-ordinator, usually a senior member of staff.

Your School **SEND** Co-ordinator is...

Tips...

THINKING ABOUT

SPECIAL EDUCATIONAL NEEDS

Look at your School SEND register and write down the needs of learners in your classes.

When you identify the range of needs your learners have, seek out your **SEND** Coordinator and other **SEND** support staff. Ask for advice to help you support SEND learners.

THE THINGS KIDS Say

Use this page to write down all the weird and hilarious things that students have said in your class.

Gifted and Talented learners are (most often) identified as those achieving above average point scores in early key stages and predicted to do as well in later key stages.

??? As a teacher what do you need to be doing?

Identify

using data provided by school.

Engage

using well planned activities

Stretch & Challenge

using well planned extension challenges.

...Working with Gifted & talented Students...

How do you most easily and effectivly do these? find out here →

SUPPORTING HIGH ACHIEVERS

Board Pen. Que Stick

Plan to Provide challenge !!

* deepen students' understanding through structured research tasks.

* Challenge students by using Bloom's action Verbs!

See page 21 on how to set better questions.

Tools which help you give good feedback →

Stamps

Sticky notes

Coloured pens.

Highlighters

Tasking Students to "do 5 more questions" is not a good example of planned challenge for your high achievers.

① ② ③

Doing more does not stretch and Challenge learners!

ADVICE

Plan work for learners which challenges them to think deeper about their Work and Show their level of understanding.

look to Bloom's taxonomy for ways to stretch and Challenge

Verbs which stretch and Challenge...

Explain · Evaluate · Compare · Create · design · Rate · Justify

63

Your actions should have a positive IMPACT on the progress of all your learners.

Constructive AFL and feedback is the most powerful tool in helping learners make good progress.

AFL = Progress

Skip ahead to the AFL section of this book to help students' progress in a number of ways

Tools to help you give good feedback

Remember: to make feedback most effective it has to be SMART

Stamps

Sticky notes

Coloured pens

Highlighters

SPECIFIC
MEASURABLE
ATTAINABLE
REALISTIC
TIMEBOUND

AFL
ASSESSMENT FOR LEARNING

GOOD
Feedback which gives clear areas for improvement. Also sets time-bound goals.

BAD
"Good"
"Wrong"
"Correct this!"

UGLY
× ✓
BANG
No written feedback!

Assessment for learning is about moving learners forward, helping them make progress!

BEST PRACTICE ADVICE!

Ticks and Crosses...
This is poor AFL because these don't tell learners what is wrong or what they need to do to IMPROVE their work! So where's the progress?

1 Brush up on your questioning technique! This will help you pose questions which challenge and stretch learners to progress.

2 Use simple structures like 'what went well?' and 'even better if...' These help you highlight good aspects of work, and the vital areas to improve, enabling progress.

More AFL advice later

MAKING YOUR MARKING COUNT

Your marking is only worth doing if it's going to have **IMPACT**

There are <u>many</u> ways to mark work and give good feedback to your learners.

One framework for giving feedback which makes learners <u>act</u> is to give feedback in 4 parts.

👍 Praise achievements in work

✋ <u>Suggest</u> areas for improvement.

❓ Pose a question to be answered by the student.

⏱ Make suggested improvements time-bound.

PRAISE

& Reward

Positive praise is about recognising the achievement of your learners no matter how **Large** or small

"Well done!"

"Excellent!"

"Fantastic!"

Use Positive Praise Language as often as you can in your lessons!

"Great work!"

REWARDS

Positive Praise can give a struggling student the confidence boost they need to really excel!

Be creative!
Students appreciate a range of reward strategies!

Pens

Stamps

Time

Stickers

Sweets

MORE PRAISE

Don't underestimate the {JOY} that your praise can bring to even your most difficult learners! Use positive praise to win them over! ☺

{Tip}

Create a typed letter for Positive Praise, save it on your USB stick!

make the letter fairly generic so that you can easily add specific praise detail.

{Tip}

Create and Save

Well done!

a range of certificates too! Learners LOVE certificates!

MORE ON AFL

Easy Peer Assessment

Have learners **swap** books and use criteria to asses each others work

WHOLE CLASS ASSESSMENT.

Simple coloured cards can help you gauge the Progress made by a class.

R G

GOOD ASSESSMENT ENABLES GOOD PROGRES

ADD YOUR AFL TIPS.

"HOW DO YOU FEEL ABOUT TODAY'S WORK?"

3 THINGS I KNOW ABOUT...

Simple sticky not assessment.

Assessment scales.

Check ou the #AFL hashtag on TWITTER too!

TRACKING PROGRESS

CONVERSATION WITH LEARNERS.

Write a list of all the classes or courses you need to 'track'.

EASY + EFFECTIVE

TRACKING PROGRESS DOESN'T NEED TO BE COMPLICATED...

HEADINGS TO INCLUDE

* LEARNER NAME
* TARGET GRADE
* CRITERIA TO BE COVERED
* YOU MIGHT ALSO RECORD THE INTERVENTIONS USED TO SUPPORT LEARNERS.

What is INTERVENTION?

In a nutshell, this is about identifying a learner who is struggling and taking action to improve their progress.

TARGETING LEARNERS

→ PUPIL PREMIUM.
+ HIGH ATTAINERS.
* UNDER ACHIEVERS.

INTERVENTION ACTIONS THAT WORK

TAKING ACTION

MONITORING THEIR PROGRESS

TIP Don't wait for Summer term to intervene.

INTERVENTION
best advice...

Make sure learners know their target grades - Stick them in their folders or books!

TARGET GRADE.

Stay on TARGET!

Give learners a space in which to record ongoing grades.

current grades...

Review targets and progress grades often.

Take action that has impact!

ACTION

try these...

Sit struggling learners with those who are most able and utilise pairing activities in class

Set **SMART** intervention targets for any learner who is in danger of falling behind.

RESULTS DAY...

GCSE

SATS

A LEVEL

GO IN TO SCHOOL BEFORE LEARNERS.

SPEAK TO SLT + HoD ABOUT ACHIEVEMENT.

GREET LEARNERS WITH A SMILE.

BE READY TO PRAISE PROGRESS AS WELL AS ACHIEVEMENT.

HAVE TISSUES TO HAND FOR THE TEARS OF JOY AND UPSET.

A*

PASS

1

MERIT

4

A*

6

Jot down random ideas, doodles, or just scribble.

Parental Engagement

Get parents as involved as you can in the education of their child. Try some of these tips...

A parent's whole world is the child you teach. Remember that the

Make sure you've access to parental email addresses

Email

Consider setting up class email groups to share positive news with parents.

meet face to face as soon as you can.

Call home as often as you can to communicate with parents and guardians.

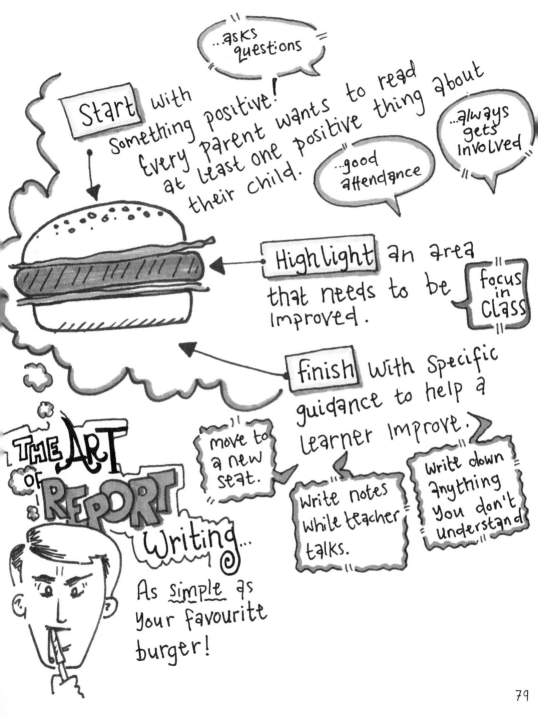

PARENTS' EVENING

SMILE LOTS!

AND BE HONEST!

HAVE EVIDENCE WITH YOU!

make a list...

things to have with me...

things to mention

1st Parents' Evening

Part two

"Please let there be something we can be proud of!"

Try to call parents and inform them of the evening

Parents want to know that their son or daughter is doing well in some way at school. Always try hard to have something positive to say, even about the most difficult students.

this allows you to build a positive relationship with parents & carers early on.

Your Role...

HELP

Future.

Help parents to see that you see potential in their child, and that it's your joint job to nurture that potential.

81

Count your tea and coffee

Every time you sip a cup, make a doodle note here...

UNDER PRESSURE...

WHEN YOU START TO FEEL THE PRESSURE **TALK** TO SOMEONE!

SOME TIPS

DON'T LET WORRIES LINGER! SOLVE THINGS BEFORE YOU GO HOME.

TRY TO HAVE A DIVIDING LINE BETWEEN WORK AND HOME.

TRY YOGA!
— NO REALLY, TRY YOGA!!

TRY TO PIN POINT THE CAUSE(S)

MARKING
PLANNING
ADMINISTRATION
STUDENTS
STAFF...

TRY TO BE SOLUTION FOCUSED
↳ TRY WHAT PEOPLE SUGGEST.

THINK WELL BE WELL, STAY WELL!

83

Well-being aware

talk to Someone!

So this week...

Everyone needs a sounding board!

Stress lowering Suggestions.

- make after work coffee with a friend a regular date in your diary.

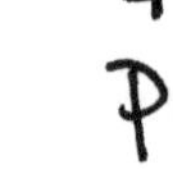

- Plan in pairs and mark in pairs! Take sweets

- Join a gym with a friend or take up a new Sport.

managing your Emotions.

KEEP CALM AND CARRY ON

From time to time every Job feels like it's too tough. But that's rarely true!

Here are some ways you can keep positive when emotions run high...

Count to 10.

Drink water. Sip it slowly to restore your claim. H2O

Talk to Someone and gain perspective.

Try hard to get exercise daily! Just 30 minutes could help you 'workout' your day.

 for me it's 6AM gym session before work

Anger page!

Get all your anger out in doodle form!

HEALTHY LIVING

eat healthy
drink healthy
be active
work-life balance

set your own goals for a healthy year

If you're Sick...

Firstly, follow school procedure!

Accept that everyone will get sick from time to time.

COVER If you can send in cover work which keeps learners on task then do so!

Keep People in the loop!

A text or a call to your boss is a must!

If you're off more than one day try to let work know asap!

Why I think having work email on your phone may be a bad idea for you!!

It's more about well-being than you think!

TRY A NO email DAY...

Write down what you get done.

Having a Social life.

Work/life balance is hugely important, spending quality time with family and friends is one way to keep balance, but doing something you can claim as your 'me' time is also important.

Join a gym.

Try an artist pursuit.

Listen to audio books.

Take up a new hobby.

Here are some suggested 'me' time activities to get you started, add your own and share it with other teachers.

Keep a list of books you've read and intend to read.

Pay day Plans... £

You've waited for pay day, what are your plans for your pay?

THINK...
HOLIDAY

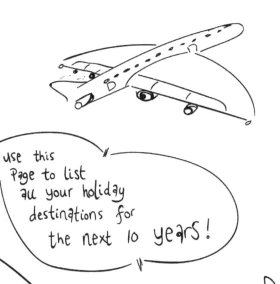

use this page to list all your holiday destinations for the next 10 years!

Sketch your day out in the sun

Colour this page to de-stress.

97

Achieve a <u>Zen-like</u> calm by completing this doodl

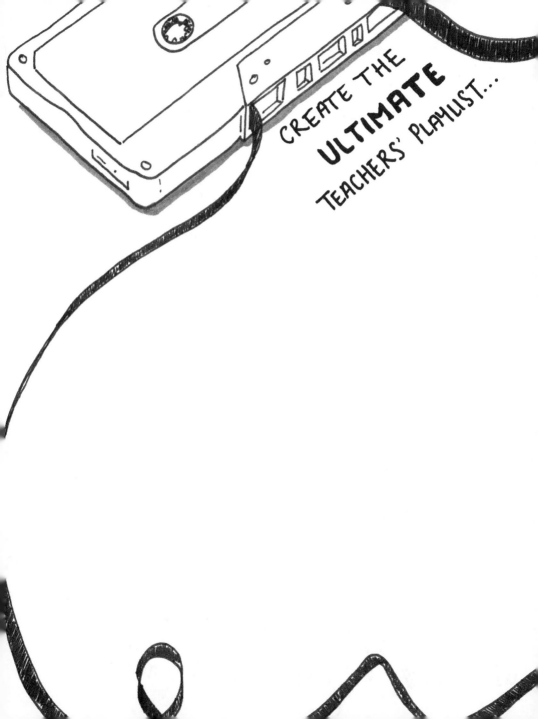

CREATE THE **ULTIMATE** TEACHERS' PLAYLIST...

Making friends in the Staffroom

that tough 1st day in a new school and role.

Explore!
Break & Lunch get out and about and about around school.

Put your head around doors!

Smile

Get to know the reception + administrative staff in school.

welcome

Good morning! say hello to everyone you meet.

from me to everyone

choc

Why not introduce yourself by leaving sweets in the staffroom with a welcoming note.

DEPARTMENT MEETINGS

* Go with a copy of the agenda.

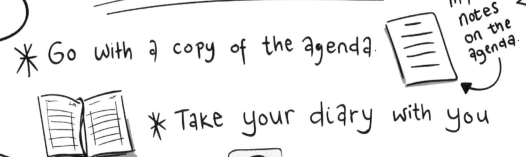

make notes on the agenda.

* Take your diary with you

* Ask questions ?

* Contribute, based on the previous or coming week.

* Keep your agenda notes in a folder and make sure you 'action' items

MAKING BEST USE OF TA's.

Hidden NINJAS of the Classroom

Often your underestimated ally in the classroom.

Get to know the support team in your School.

Get to know their strengths AND their SKILLS.

General TA NINJA!
* All round skill set.
* Valued asset in any class.

Specialist TA NINJA!
* Supporting a specific student.
* Specific skill set.
* Asset for inclusion & progress.

Simple tips to follow...

* Be clear
* Be realistic
* Share plans
* Share ideas

find two TAs in shool that you don't work with and get to know their role!

Name + Special Skill

How do you Show your appreciation? write down all the ways you say thank you.

ADMINISTRATION APPRECIATION

Always be thankful for the support in your school.

Look Over the Fence...

ONE OF THE BEST WAYS TO LEARN IS TO OBSERVE OTHERS...

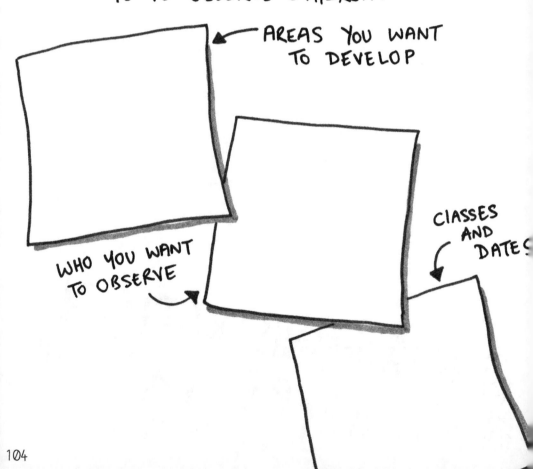

AREAS YOU WANT TO DEVELOP

WHO YOU WANT TO OBSERVE

CLASSES AND DATES

the Unofficial Mentors.

Who are your unofficial mentors, and Why?

WHO | Why

We all like to be praised, leave this page on the desk of someone you admire.

create a certificate for a colleague.

REASONS TO USE TWITTER...
follow for AMAZING ICT inspiration!!
@ICT evangelist
Follow for latest whole school news + much more
@Teacher toolkit
FIND NEW IDEAS!
FIND THINGS WHICH MAKE YOU THINK!
Access expert advice in seconds!!
Keep up to date! with news + trends.
Discuss
Be part of educational discussions.
KEEP YOUR DIGITAL PROFILE POSITIVE!!
Best advice!
Follow 'BIG' chats via #hashtags
#ukedchat
#NQTchat
#SLTcha

Why tweet teach?

Twitter is a Social Media, be careful when using it.
- Ask your School about their social media **Policy** for advice.

💡 At its heart, ♡ Twitter is about Sharing ideas.

I ♡ ideas

worldwide 🌍))) (((ideas.

Twitter is Web-based so you can use it from any device.

ⓛ Share and find ideas at any time of day or night.

🔍 Search:
#ukedchat
#Edchat
#Edchattie

Setting up your account.

- Choose a Profile image. (Something you'd be happy for other teachers to see).

 Bio... - Write something about you as a Professional.

 Search- for other teachers to 'Follow'.

Who to follow on twitter

This is to help you get started

All of these people have inspired me!

@Urban_teacher

@Teachertoolkit

@ASTsupportAALi

@UKEdMag

me!

@PiW2tweets

@ICTmagic

Add your own tweeting teachers and then photocopy this page

SHARE COPIES in the staffroom.

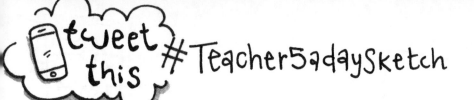

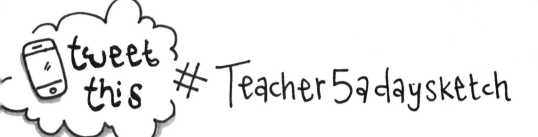

Teacher 5 a day sketch

Sketch something creative.

Sketch something natural.

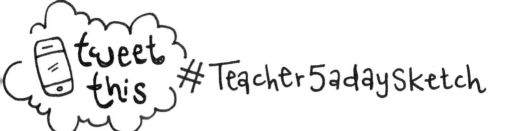

tweet this #Teacher5adaySketch

"Sketch something or someone living."

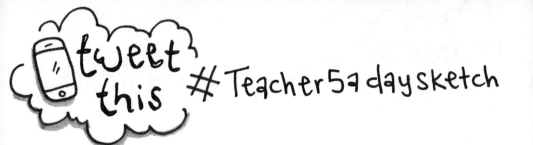

Sketch something you can see from a window.

#Teacher5adaySketch

"Sketch something unusual wearing a tie."

Sketch something you find on your desk.

WEBSITES
+ BLOGS...
Keep a list of important sites
(like exam boards!)

Teach meets

Dedicated teachers Organising their Own CPD!

The trick is to share small ideas/tips which have positive impact!

> Write down one idea on this sticky note.

The key is that it's about INFORMAL Sharing of ideas!

Use this Sticky note to Jot down ideas you'd Share at teach meets.

Search ↓

#teachmeet via Social media.

OR

Type 'teachmeetuk' into a Search engin

find at Least One to attend this year.

Guest Speakers

Prof Brian Cox *explains* GCSE Physics

Guest Speakers can bring your subject to life and inspire your students. Make two lists here of both dream guest speakers and real world guests.

Dream guests

Real World guests

Knowing you're part of a bigger network.

LEGAL Advice
contracts
conditions
pay

Career advice and guidance.

HELP!
Help, support and advice.
L
when you need it!

Family financial advice.
MONEY BOX

Benefits of a UNION

HAVE YOU JOINED A UNION ?

They do more than **Strike** people join union for many reasons, what are yours?

Submit a Story to your School newsletter.

what's the latest and best news from your classes?

Teachers' Daily News.

Headline

Photo

REFLECTION
Key to Success!

Ask yourself these questions as a start to your reflection.

Did the activity allow everyone to progress?

Did all students benefit from the activity/lesson?

What did I aim to achieve with this activity?

What evidence was produced to show real progress?

Did the actual outcome match the expected outcome?

Where did this fit within my scheme of work?

Speak to your mentor or line manager and set yourself 3 challenging targets to work towards.

As well as your students making progress towards their targets, it's important that you as a teacher can make your own professional progress towards your own targets!

It's about Professional GROWTH!

PROFESSIONAL PROGRESS

(A good tool for NQT's)

Skill tracking...

You'll develop many skills this year. It may help you to keep track of new things you do, challenges you overcome and new skills that you acquire.

Use this page to start jotting them down.

↪

NQTs
I wish I'd known...

Stupid Questions?

NO SUCH THING!

 Be as open as you can be when you've questions to ask.

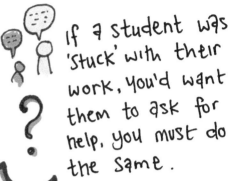 If a student was 'stuck' with their work, you'd want them to ask for help, you must do the same.

?

What questions did you have at the start of this year..?

Keep a note of mistakes AND their solutions.

IF YOU MAKE A MISTAKE...

Always speak to someone!

Showing the best of you...

As your year goes on and your confidence grows, you'll start to feel you've ideas and skills that you want to share!

1.
Create an 'In my classroom' wall display to showcase what you're proud of!

3. Share an idea over a coffee in the staff room.

idea fuel

2.
come watch me teach

Invite people to informally watch a lesson of your choosing.

- What do you enjoy?
- What always goes well?
- What do learners respond well to?
- What gets praised when you're observed?

think..

KNOW YOURSELF...

Why do you teach?
? ? ? ? ?

I'm here, I'm a teacher because...

_____

_____

_____

_____

_____

_____

_____

_____

_____

_____

_____

_____

_____

_____

_____

_____

_____

your career plan...

5 years

where do you want to
be and what would you
like to have achieved

10 years

15 years

PROMOTION OPPORTUNITIES

THINKING ABOUT YOUR CAREER.

Leadership doesn't have to mean Head of department

As your year comes to an end start to think about how you can continue to contribute to your whole school or subject area by leading a specific aspect of school life.

Think about what you enjoy and are good at.

consider

Using ICT to support learning

Working with high or low ability learners

Sharing AFL Strategies

Working with key stages.

TALK TO YOUR MENTOR + LINE MANAGER FOR ADVICE.

137

Applying for Jobs.

How to stand out from the crowd!

GIVE YOUR CV A COLOURFUL APPEARENCE!

Your CV should showcase your character before you visit the school you've applied to. It's you (on paper) so make it stand out! Consider adding a **photo** to your cv (make sure to smile). Carefully consider a more creative layout and colour scheme too.

Doodle cv ideas on this page!

THE INTERVIEW

How to show your best side.

① Read up in advance about the school, its reputation and Ofsted reports.

② Practise the best way you can, explain your impact on the progress and the achievement of your students.

③ Ask your current school to provide you with a mock interview. A useful way to prepare for the process.

CREATE A CERTIFICATE FOR ONE OF YOUR ACHIEVEMENTS

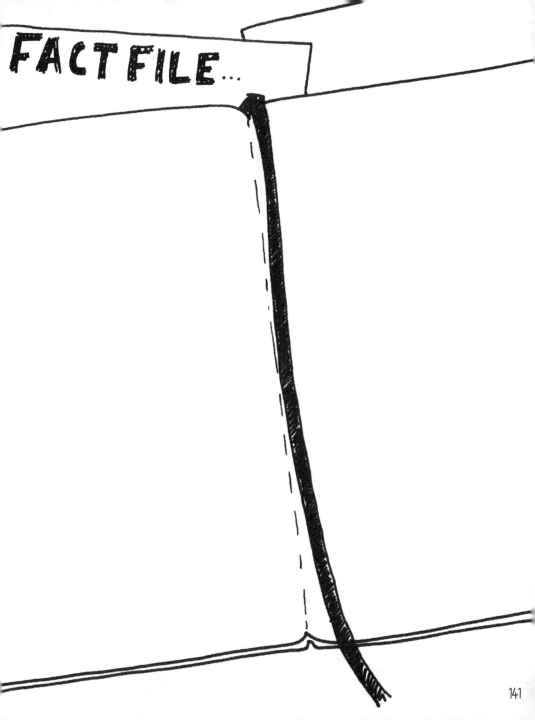

FACT FILE...

FACT FILE...

INDEX